Theory Paper Grade 8   2007   A

Duration 3 hours

Candidates should answer all FIVE questions.
Write your answers on this paper — no others will be accepted.
Answers must be written clearly and neatly — otherwise marks may be lost.

TOTAL MARKS
100

1 Complete the violin parts in the following extract adapted from a trio sonata by Corelli, following the figuring shown under the basso continuo.

3

2 Complete the given outline of the following passage, adapted from a piano piece by H. Lemoine (1786–1854).

Moderato

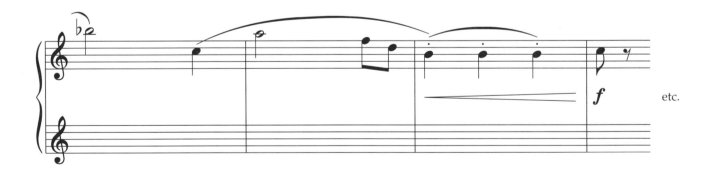

etc.

3 Compose a complete melody of not less than twelve bars using **ONE** of the following openings and for the given unaccompanied instrument. Continue in the same style and include appropriate performance directions. Write the complete melody on the staves below.

[20]

TROMBONE

OBOE

Largo e mesto

4 Look at the extract printed opposite, which is from a piano sonata, and then answer the questions below.

(a) Give the meaning of:

Largo e mesto ...Slow and... (2)

rinf. (e.g. bar 9) .... (2)

(b) Mark **clearly** on the score, using the appropriate capital letter for identification, one example of each of the following. Also give the bar number of each of your answers.

In bars 1–13

A the melodic interval of a diminished 4th in
the left-hand part (circle the notes concerned). Bar .... (2)

B a chromatic lower auxiliary note in the left-hand part that forms the interval
of a compound diminished 7th (diminished 14th) with the right-hand part. Bar .... (2)

From bar 14 onwards

C a false (cross) relation in the right-hand part (circle the notes concerned). Bar .... (2)

D a bar that contains three different positions of the same diminished 7th chord. Bar .... (2)

E an upward-resolving chromatic appoggiatura in the melody (circle the note concerned).

Bar .... (2)

(c) Write out in full the right-hand part of bar 11 as you think it should be played.

(6)

(d) Identify the chord marked * in bar 18 by writing on the dotted lines below. Use either words or symbols. Indicate the position of the chord, whether it is major, minor, augmented or diminished, and name the prevailing key.

Chord .... Key .... (4)

(e) From the following list, underline the name of the most likely composer of this extract.

Chopin   J. S. Bach   Beethoven   (1)

5 Study the extract printed on pages 9–10, which is from Liszt's *Faust-Symphonie*, and then
answer the questions below.

| 25 |

(a) Give the meaning of:

Tenorposaunen ....Tenor trombones.. (2)

Pauken in E, H ....Timpani in E and B.. (3)

(b) (i) Write out the parts for trumpets in bars 1–2 as they would sound at concert pitch.

(3)

(ii) Using the blank stave at the foot of page 10, write out the parts for clarinets in bars 5–7
as they would sound at concert pitch. (5)

(c) Mark **clearly** on the score, using the appropriate capital letter for identification, one example
of each of the following. Also give the bar number of each of your answers.

A a triple stop where the outer two notes form the interval of a
compound major 2nd (major 9th) (circle the notes concerned). Bar .... (2)

B the harmonic interval of an augmented 2nd
sounding between two double-reed instruments. Bar .... (2)

C the melodic interval of a compound minor 2nd
(minor 9th) played by a single-reed instrument. Bar .... (2)

D a complete diminished 7th chord in second inversion played by the horns. Bar ...5..... (2)

(d) Answer TRUE or FALSE to the following statements:

(i) The string parts from bar 1 (beat 2) to the end of
bar 2 are repeated exactly in bars 3 (beat 2) to 4. ...F............... (2)

(ii) In bar 5, the third and fourth horns *sound* at the same pitch as the violas. ...F............... (2)

9

(b) (ii)

Clarinets, bars 5–7

Theory Paper Grade 8   2007   B

Duration 3 hours

TOTAL MARKS
100

Candidates should answer all FIVE questions.
Write your answers on this paper — no others will be accepted.
Answers must be written clearly and neatly — otherwise marks may be lost.

1 Complete the violin parts in the following extract adapted from a trio sonata by Corelli, following the figuring shown under the basso continuo.

15

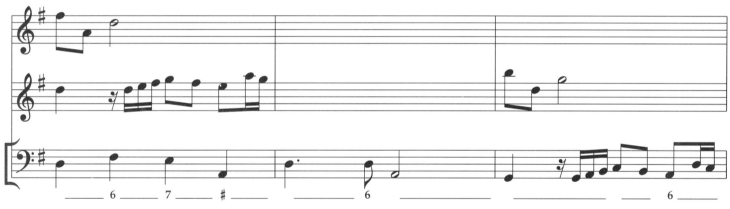

etc.

2 Complete the given outline of the following passage, adapted from a piano piece by
J. W. Hässler (1747–1822).

3 Compose a complete melody of not less than twelve bars using **ONE** of the following openings and for the given unaccompanied instrument. Continue in the same style and include appropriate performance directions. Write the complete melody on the staves below.

4 Look at the extract from a piano piece, printed opposite, and then answer the questions below. [25]

(a) Identify the chords marked * in bars 6 and 29 by writing on the dotted lines below. Use either words or symbols. Indicate the position of each chord, whether it is major, minor, augmented or diminished, and name the prevailing key for each chord.

Bar 6 .... Key .... (4)

Bar 29 .... Key .... (4)

(b) Complete the following statements:

The extract begins in the key of F minor and the first modulation is in bars .... to

the key of .... The second modulation is to the key of ....

in bars .... (4)

(c) Write out in full the right-hand part of bar 19 as you think it should be played.

(3)

(d) Mark **clearly** on the score, using the appropriate capital letter for identification, one example of each of the following. Also give the bar number(s) of each of your answers.

A a bar that contains an enharmonic change in
the left-hand part (circle the notes concerned). Bar .... (2)

B a false (cross) relation (circle the notes concerned). Bar .... (2)

C a tonic pedal lasting for three bars (mark ⌐ C ⌐ over the bars). Bars .... (2)

D two simultaneous notes of anticipation a 3rd apart (circle the notes concerned). Bar .... (2)

(e) From the following list, underline the name of the most likely composer of this extract.

Brahms   Grieg   Debussy   Chopin (2)

5 Study the orchestral extract printed on pages 17–18 and then answer the questions below. [25]

(a) Give the meaning of:

Moins animé (e.g. bar 2) .... (2)

Assez (e.g. bar 5) .... (1)

Pressez (bar 9) .... (2)

(b) Write out the following parts as they would sound at concert pitch, and using the given clefs.

(i) Horns, bar 1

(4)

(ii) First and second clarinets in A, bars 4–5

(2)

(c) Describe in full how the cellos are instructed to play bar 9.

....

.... (3)

(d) Complete the following statements:

(i) Another name for Flûte en sol is .... (2)

(ii) The divided violas sound a major 3rd apart for the whole of bar .... (2)

(iii) On the first beat of bar 2, the three instruments playing the *lowest sounding* notes are the

...., the .... and the .... (3)

(e) Rewrite bars 2–3 of the *first* flute part in compound time but without changing the rhythmic effect. Remember to include both of the new time signatures.

(4)

17

Theory Paper Grade 8   2007   C

Duration 3 hours

Candidates should answer all FIVE questions.
Write your answers on this paper — no others will be accepted.
Answers must be written clearly and neatly — otherwise marks may be lost.

1   Complete the violin and oboe parts in the following extract adapted from a trio sonata
    by Albinoni, following the figuring shown under the basso continuo.

15

2 Complete the given outline of the following passage adapted from a piano piece by Fibich (1850–1900). 15

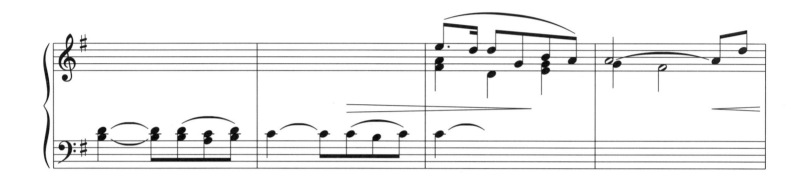

3 Compose a complete melody of not less than twelve bars using **ONE** of the following openings and for the given unaccompanied instrument. Continue in the same style and include appropriate performance directions. Write the complete melody on the staves below.

4 Look at the extract printed opposite, which is from the first of Grieg's *Poetic Tone-Pictures*, Op. 3, and then answer the questions below.

(a) Identify the chords marked ⌈ ∗ ⌉ in bars 16 and 37 by writing on the dotted lines below. Use either words or symbols. Indicate the position of each chord and whether it is major, minor, augmented or diminished. The key is E minor.

Bar 16 .... ⎫ (3)

Bar 37 .... ⎬ Key: E minor

⎭ (3)

(b) Complete the following statement concerning notes of melodic decoration (e.g. changing notes):

The only note in the right-hand part of bar 21 that is *essential* to the harmony is .... The

only *unessential* note in bar 22 is .... and this is called a(n) .... (3)

(c) Mark **clearly** on the score, using the appropriate capital letter for identification, one example of each of the following. Also give the bar number(s) of each of your answers.

A a dominant pedal (not sustained) lasting for
five bars (mark ⌊___A___⌋ under the bars). Bars .... (2)

B a chromatic upward-resolving appoggiatura
in the right-hand part (circle the note). Bar .... (2)

C the melodic interval of a diminished 3rd in
the right-hand part (circle the notes concerned). Bar(s) .... (2)

(d) Compare bars 25–28 with bars 33–36 and then answer the questions below.

(i) What is the most significant similarity?... (2)

(ii) What is the most significant difference in:

1. rhythm? .... (2)

2. harmony? .... (2)

(e) Rewrite the right-hand part of bar 31 in compound time but without changing the rhythmic effect. Remember to include the new time signature.

(4)

5 Study the orchestral extract printed on pages 25–26 and then answer the questions below.

(a) Give the meaning of:

Langsam .... (2)

tr~~~~~~ (e.g. timpani, bar 1) .... (2)

zart (violas, bar 7) .... (2)

(b) (i) Write out the part for second clarinet in bars 3–7 as it would sound at concert pitch.

(3)

(ii) Using the blank staves at the foot of page 26, write out the parts for horns in bar 10 as they would sound at concert pitch. Remember that they are in different keys. (5)

(c) Complete the following statements:

(i) The phrase played by the violas in bars 7–8 is imitated immediately by the ....

.... in bars .... and again in modified form by the same instrument in

bars .... and bars .... (4)

(ii) The harmonic interval formed by the first bassoon and English horn notes on the first

beat of bar 13 is a(n) .... (2)

(d) Identify the chord marked * in bar 7 (shaded) by writing on the dotted line below. Use either words or symbols. Indicate the position of the chord and whether it is major, minor, augmented or diminished. The key is F major.

Chord .... Key: F major (3)

(e) From the following list, underline the name of the most likely composer of this extract and give a reason for your answer.

            Puccini   Brahms   Wagner   Elgar (1)

Reason:

.... (1)

25

etc.

(b)   (ii)   Horns, bar 10

Theory Paper Grade 8   2007   S

Duration 3 hours

Candidates should answer all FIVE questions.
Write your answers on this paper — no others will be accepted.
Answers must be written clearly and neatly — otherwise marks may be lost.

1 Complete the violin parts in the following extract adapted from a trio sonata by Corelli, following the figuring shown under the basso continuo.   15

2 Complete the given outline of the following passage from a piano piece by Grechaninov (1864–1956). 15

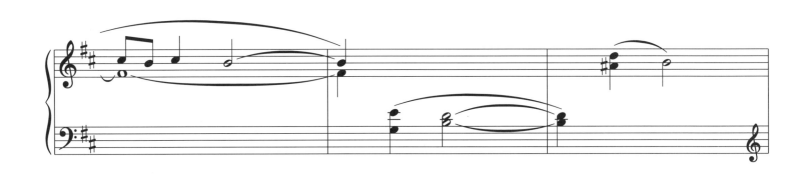

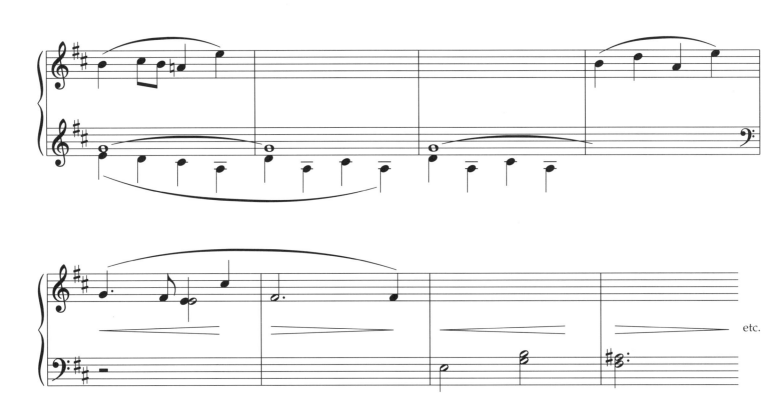

3 Compose a complete melody of not less than twelve bars using **ONE** of the following openings and for the given unaccompanied instrument. Continue in the same style and include appropriate performance directions. Write the complete melody on the staves below.

4 Look at the extract printed opposite, which is from R. Strauss's Cello Sonata, and then answer the questions below.

(a) Identify the chords marked * in bars 23 and 30 by writing on the dotted lines below. Use either words or symbols. Indicate the position of each chord, whether it is major, minor, augmented or diminished, and name the prevailing key in bar 30.

Bar 23 .... Key: G minor   (3)

Bar 30 .... Key ....   (4)

(b) Mark **clearly** on the score, using the appropriate capital letter for identification, one example of each of the following. Also give the bar number(s) of each of your answers.

From bar 20 onwards

A a dominant inner (middle) pedal (not sustained) lasting for four bars. Bars ....   (2)

B a falling chromatic semitone (augmented unison)
in the cello part (circle the notes conerned). Bar(s) ....   (2)

C syncopation in the right-hand and left-hand piano parts lasting for half a bar. Bar ....   (2)

D a false (cross) relation in the right-hand piano part (circle the notes concerned). Bar ....   (2)

(c) Complete the following statements:

(i) The opening theme (bars 1–8) returns in bars ...., two differences in the cello part being

being .... and ....,

and one difference in the piano part being ....   (4)

(ii) *molto con espress.* (bar 26) means ....   (2)

(d) Using the given tenor clef, rewrite the cello part of bars 6–7 in compound time but without changing the rhythmic effect. Remember to include the new time signature.

(4)

31

5 Study the symphonic extract printed on pages 33–34 and then answer the questions below. | 25 |

   (a) Give the meaning of:

      Scherzo .... (2)

      Molto vivace .... (2)

      tr~~~~~ (e.g. timpani, bar 9) .... (2)

   (b) Mark **clearly** on the score, using the appropriate capital letter for identification, one example of each of the following. Also give the bar number of each of your answers.

      A   the melodic interval of a diminished 4th played by
          a double-reed instrument (circle the notes concerned). Bar .... (2)

      B   a triple-stop where the two outer notes form the
          interval of a compound minor 3rd (minor 10th). Bar .... (2)

   (c) Write out the parts for clarinets and trumpets in bars 9–13 (first note) as they would sound at concert pitch.

Clarinets   (4)

Trumpets   (3)

   (d) Complete the following statements:

      (i)   The first violins have an accented passing note (appoggiatura) in bar .... and an upper auxiliary note in bar .... (2)

      (ii) An alternative abbreviated rhythmic notation for the first violin part in bar 9 is .... (2)

      (iii) There is a dominant 7th chord in second inversion in the subdominant minor key in bar(s)

            .... (2)

      (iv) There is a 4–3 suspension in the first violin part in bar .... (2)

Scherzo